THE
CALM
JOURNAL

An exclusive edition for

ALLSORTED.

WD19 4BG, U.K.

This edition first published in Great Britain in 2022
An exclusive edition for

ALLSORTED.

WD19 4BG, U.K.

This Calm journal will encourage you to
make time for yourself in this busy world.
With activities and inspiration to help you
to de-stress and appreciate all the
little things in life.

Follow the prompts to calm your mind
and enjoy your life more.

You'll soon be able to slow down,
live life in the moment and
discover a calmer, more positive life.

Make yourself a
priority

My journey towards calm starts here.

I'm feeling...

Picture every aspect of your life right now
and write down all the positives on these pages...

Learn to

STOP

(sit, think, observe, plan)

for 5 minutes a day

to focus on yourself.

*My goals
for a calmer
mind*

NOTES

The
quieter
you are,
the more
you
hear

What are you grateful for today?

Write five things that have
made you smile today...

NOTES

NOTES

Write a list of little promises to yourself...

Write a list of big promises to yourself...

Write 3 things in the past that you
want to let go of...

Write 3 things you're looking forward to...

NOTES

NOTES

One thing
at a time

NOTES

What is your most enjoyable way to spend the day?

Who is the most supportive person in your life
and what do you do to thank them?

What do you
want to do in
the next month?

What do you
want to do in
the next year?

NOTES

NOTES

Live in the
present

What are you grateful for today?

Write five things that have made you smile today...

Call a friend or family member for
an overdue catch up.

What did you talk about?

TAKE A RELAXING WALK

Where did you go and what did you see?

NOTES

NOTES

CREATE A SOOTHING PLAYLIST

When life feels overwhelming,
put this on to help relax your mind

Take time
to make
your soul
smile

Spend time on a crafty or creative project

Inspiration...

Ideas...

To-do list...

Declutter a room in your house

Healthy
body,
happy
mind

Plan your meals for the next week

Switch off all notifications for an afternoon

NOTES

NOTES

NOTES

Old ways
don't open
new doors

HOW ARE YOU FEELING TODAY?

Do a task you've been putting off

WRITE DOWN

A big thing on your mind...

One thing that could help...

What's stopping you moving on?

What are you grateful for today?

Write five things that have made you smile today...

NOTES

NOTES

NOTES

When do you

feel most

relaxed?

Who inspires
you and why?

Relax
Refresh
Reconnect

Write the words you need to hear...

NOTES

NOTES

Make each day your
masterpiece

HOW ARE YOU FEELING TODAY?

What do you do in your everyday life
to care for your body and mind?

What self-care activities can you do to decompress and relax into a calm state of mind?

Make a list of everything you want

to say 'no' to...

Make a list of everything you want

to say 'yes' to...

Now check a few off your list!

NOTES

NOTES

*Let your breath
untie knots
in your mind,
body and soul*

Practice mindful breathing...

Sit in a quiet area, inside or out,
and close your eyes.
Concentrate on what you hear and feel,
and let your breath deepen.

Let your breath cycle lengthen
to approximately 6 seconds
and let go of your thoughts,
concentrating solely on your breathing.
Continue as long as you feel comfortable –
this simple meditation will help increase
inner peace, well-being and happiness.

Learn to do just one thing at a time.

If you're eating, just eat.

If you're walking, just walk.

TAKE A MOMENT

What can you...

Hear

See

Smell

Touch

Taste

Allow what
you feel to
simply *be*

NOTES

NOTES

NOTES

Write down a memory that always

makes you smile...

Appreciate all the little things around you
on a walk you know well.

What new things did you notice?

It's the
little things
that make life
beautiful

What are you grateful for today?

Write five things that have made you smile today...

What parts of your life are most distracting?

How can you reduce these distractions
to improve your sense of peace?

Quiet the
mind
and the soul
will *speak*

NOTES

NOTES

NOTES

When was the last time you got lost in a book?

HOW ARE YOU FEELING TODAY?

Happiness
is an
inside
job

A little place for all your thoughts

When was the last time you laughed at work?

NOTES

Choose a chore you do every day
and give your fully focused attention to it.

What

did you

notice?

CLEAR YOUR ONLINE CLUTTER

Unsubscribe from unwanted emails
and tidy up your desktop.

Breathe
Step back
Think
Then react

NOTES

Choose a chore you do every day
and give your fully focused attention to it

SLOW DOWN

Spend less time rushing and more time thinking – whether that's while walking, eating or working.

NOTES

NOTES

TAKE A MOMENT

What can you...

Hear

See

Smell

Touch

Taste

The
best way to
capture a moment
is to
pay **attention**
to it

Gather your thoughts and discover
what's really worrying you

Big deal...

Little worry...

What can I let go?

NOTES

What are you grateful for today?

Write five things that have
made you smile today...

NOTES

Take it
day
by day

NOTES

WHAT DO YOU WANT
TO ACCOMPLISH...

Today...

Tomorrow...

Next week...

What stresses you out and what can you do
to reduce this stress?

What activities do you enjoy doing which also help you clear your mind?

How can you rebalance your day
to make more time for them?

What is one thing you look forward to every day?

Smile *big*
laugh
often

NOTES

NOTES

How would you describe yourself to a stranger?

HOW ARE YOU FEELING TODAY?

Actually, you can

List three things you would do

if you had no fear...

Now
pluck up
the courage
to do one!

What have you learned about yourself
and how you can feel calmer?

What were your favourite parts of this journal?

Which aspects are you going to continue with
to keep your headspace clear?

If you had the chance,
what would you say to yourself if you
were just starting this journal?

Now write a letter for your future self,
focusing on calming activities that work for you.
Read this whenever you begin to feel overwhelmed.
Find inner peace again!

NOTES

NOTES

NOTES

NOTES

NOTES

NOTES

NOTES

NOTES

NOTES